BIBLE

journaling

& CREATIVE

WORSHIP

EMAIL US AT
modernscriptdesigns@gmail.com
TO GET FREE GOODIES!

Just title the email "Bible Journaling Goodies!"
And we will send some extra surprises your way!

INTRODUCTION

We hope this journal is a tool used to bring you into a deeper relationship with the Lord!

God himself is portrayed as Creator and creative throughout the bible. We have found that Bible Journaling brings a kind of connection to that certain characteristic of His and can create a really special quiet time with him. It is a beautiful process, and while it is about more than just the art, this journal provides a wonderful canvas to enhance your connection and quiet time with the Lord. And even though it doesn't matter if your penmanship is on point or if you perfect the color palette, writing in your bible can be very intimidating! That's why we have created this practice journal so that you can plan out your design and practice before committing it to the page in your Bible! This book can serve as a keepsake of your beautiful designs and notes or it can simply be your practice journal to get your ideas on paper first.

Remember that He doesn't care about the final product.

We also pray that this journal provides another opportunity for you to meditate on and memorize Scripture. Bible journaling provides a wonderful way to process what you are reading and commit the story or verse to memory. It is well known that one of the best ways to memorize Scripture is to write it down. On the practice pages of this journal, we have created a section for you to first simply just write down the verse you are studying before you journal or create any designs. The more you write down the verse, the more likely you will commit it to memory.

On the following pages, we'll jump in to tips and tricks to get started!

5 EASY STEPS!

① Read

OPEN YOUR BIBLE AND SPEND TIME WITH GOD!

② Pray
ASK GOD WHAT HE
WANTS TO TEACH YOU.

③ Write it down
PHYSICALLY WRITING SCRIPTURE DOWN IS AN
EXTREMELY USEFUL MEMORY AID.

④ Journal it
TAKE THE BIG IDEA FROM THE TEXT AND
GET CREATIVE WITH IT!

⑤ Date it

DATE EACH OF YOUR ENTRIES SO YOU REMEMBER
WHAT YOU WERE LEARNING IN PAST SEASONS OF LIFE.

TOOLS

The biggest challenge with Bible journaling is finding mediums that work well on thin Bible paper!
Here are a few favorite tools:

Good Pencil & Eraser - *Really all you need to get started is a good pencil and eraser! The white hi-polymer erasers are wonderful for erasing your pencil sketches!*

Colored Pencils - *Prismacolor pencils have soft lead and are a great medium to easily add some color to your designs.*

Watercolor Pencils - *These pencils create a beautiful watercolor effect! Just be careful as the water may make your page slightly wrinkle.*

Pigma Microns by Sakura - *Great pens that don't bleed!*

Gel Pens- *A great pen to add color to your designs!*

Gelly Roll White Ink Pen - *Great for adding shadows and designs on top of color.*

Crayola Twistable Colored Pencils - *Don't discount Crayola products! These pencils never have to be sharpened & are soft on your Bible paper!*

Faber-Castell Gelatos - *Expensive but the results are gorgeous.*

T I P S

LETTERING TIPS:

- *Think of lettering as drawing, not writing.*

- *You do not have to have pretty handwriting to master lettering.*

- *Write slowly, take your time!*

- *Always start in pencil.*

- *Practice individual letters, then connecting letters, then designs.*

DESIGN/LAYOUT TIPS:

- *Sum up the main message of the scripture passage you are journaling. Summarize if you need!*

- *Don't worry about creating the perfect piece of art each time. The Word of God is perfection itself!*

- *Use simple illustrations and doodles to emphasize the meaning of a verse. You don't have to be a professional artist to draw!*

- *Play with color! You can often highlight your lettering artwork by adding a colored background of some sort!*

- *An easy way to distinguish between words in your design is by changing up the size. You can play around with different lettering styles and sizes to highlight certain words.*

- *Use line dividers and banners to separate certain parts of your scripture passage.*

Aa Bb Cc Dd
Ee Ff Gg Hh
Ii Jj Kk Ll
Mm Nn Oo Pp
Qq Rr Ss Tt
Uu Vv Ww Xx
Yy Zz

Aa Bb Cc Dd

Ee Ff Gg Hh

Ii Jj Kk Ll

Mm Nn Oo Pp

Qq Rr Ss Tt

Uu Vv Ww Xx

Yy Zz

Aa Bb Cc Dd

Ee Ff Gg Hh

Ii Jj Kk Ll

Mm Nn Oo Pp

Qq Rr Ss Tt

Uu Vv Ww Xx

Yy Zz

Aa Bb Cc Dd

Ee Ff Gg Hh

Ii Jj Kk Ll

Mm Nn Oo Pp

Qq Rr Ss Tt

Uu Vv Ww Xx

Yy Zz

The next section includes 10 example journaling designs to give you some ideas and get your creative juices flowing! The rest of the book includes blank layouts for you to use for your own creative adventures!

OPEN YOUR

AND GET STARTED!

We are praying for you!

WRITE IT DOWN!

JOURNAL IT!

VERSE: Isaiah 12:2

Surely God is my
salvation; I will trust and
not be afraid. The Lord,
the Lord himself, is my
strength and my defense;
he has become my
salvation.

PRAYER:

TRUST in the LORD & DO NOT be afraid

WRITE IT DOWN!

JOURNAL IT!

VERSE: Psalm 119: 102-103

I have not departed from
your laws, for you
yourself have taught me.
How sweet are your words
to my taste, sweeter
than honey to my mouth!

_____

_____

_____

_____

_____

_____

_____

_____

_____

PRAYER: ·······················

_____

_____

_____

_____

_____

_____

_____

HIS
WORDS
— are —
Sweeter
THAN
honey

VERSE: **2 Tim 1: 6-7**

For this reason I
remind you to fan into
flame the gift of God,
which is in you through
the laying on of my
hands. For the Spirit of
God does not make
us timid, but give us
power and love and
self-discipline.

PRAYER:

the
Spirit
GIVES US
POWER
love
& SELF
DISCIPLINE

VERSE: Song Of Solomon 2:4

Let him lead me to the
banquet hall, and let his
banner over me be love.

PRAYER:

His BANNER over ME is LOVE

VERSE: Rom 12: 9-13

Love must be sincere. Hate
what is evil; cling to what
is good. Be devoted to one
another in love. Honor one
another above yourselves.
Never be lacking in zeal,
but keep your spiritual
fervor, serving the Lord.
Be joyful in hope, patient
in affliction, faithful in
prayer. Share with the
Lord's people who are in
need. Practice hospitality.

PRAYER:

WRITE IT DOWN!

JOURNAL IT!

VERSE: 1 Thess 5:9-11

For God did not appoint us to suffer wrath but to receive salvation through our Lord Jesus Christ. He died for us so that, whether we are awake or asleep, we may live together with him. Therefore encourage one another and build each other up, just as in fact you are doing.

PRAYER:

VERSE: Phil 4: 4-7

Rejoice in the Lord always. I will say it again: Rejoice! Let your gentleness be evident to all. The Lord is near. Do not be anxious about anything, but in every situation, by prayer and petition, with thanksgiving, present your requests to God. And the peace of God, which transcends all understanding, will guard your hearts and your minds in Christ Jesus.

PRAYER: ··

REJOICE
always
AGAIN
I SAY
Rejoice

VERSE: Psalm 46: 10

Be still, and know that I
am God: I will be exalted
among the nations, I will
be exalted in the earth.

_____

_____

_____

_____

_____

_____

_____

_____

_____

_____

PRAYER: ....

_____

_____

_____

_____

_____

_____

_____

_____

_____

be still & KNOW I AM GOD

VERSE: Lam 3: 21-23

Yet this I call to mind
and therefore I have
hope: Because of the
Lord's great love we are
not consumed, for his
compassions never fail.
They are new every
morning: great is your
faithfulness.

PRAYER:

HIS
mercies
ARE
new
EVERY
morning

VERSE: Joshua 1: 9

Have I not commanded
you? Be strong and
courageous. Do not be
afraid; do not be
discouraged, for the Lord
your God will be with
you wherever you go.

PRAYER:

BE »»»»»
STRONG
≫≫and→
COURAGEOUS

WRITE IT DOWN!

JOURNAL IT!

VERSE:

PRAYER:

WRITE IT DOWN!

JOURNAL IT!

VERSE:

PRAYER:

WRITE IT DOWN!

JOURNAL IT!

VERSE:

_____
_____
_____
_____
_____
_____
_____
_____
_____
_____
_____
_____
_____
_____

PRAYER:

_____
_____
_____
_____
_____
_____
_____

WRITE IT DOWN!

JOURNAL IT!

VERSE:

PRAYER:

WRITE IT DOWN!

JOURNAL IT!

VERSE:

PRAYER:

WRITE IT DOWN!

JOURNAL IT!

VERSE:

PRAYER:

WRITE IT DOWN!

JOURNAL IT!

VERSE:

_____

_____

_____

_____

_____

_____

_____

_____

_____

_____

_____

_____

_____

_____

_____

_____

PRAYER:

_____

_____

_____

_____

_____

_____

_____

_____

WRITE IT DOWN!

JOURNAL IT!

VERSE:

PRAYER:

WRITE IT DOWN!

JOURNAL IT!

VERSE:

PRAYER:

WRITE IT DOWN!

JOURNAL IT!

VERSE:

PRAYER:

WRITE IT DOWN!

JOURNAL IT!

VERSE:

_____

_____

_____

_____

_____

_____

_____

_____

_____

_____

_____

_____

_____

_____

_____

PRAYER:

_____

_____

_____

_____

_____

_____

_____

WRITE IT DOWN!   JOURNAL IT!

VERSE:

_____

_____

_____

_____

_____

_____

_____

_____

_____

_____

_____

_____

_____

PRAYER: ································

_____

_____

_____

_____

_____

_____

_____

WRITE IT DOWN!

JOURNAL IT!

VERSE:

PRAYER:

WRITE IT DOWN!

JOURNAL IT!

VERSE:

_____
_____
_____
_____
_____
_____
_____
_____
_____
_____
_____
_____
_____
_____
_____

PRAYER:

_____
_____
_____
_____
_____
_____
_____

WRITE IT DOWN!

JOURNAL IT!

VERSE:

_____
_____
_____
_____
_____
_____
_____
_____
_____
_____
_____
_____
_____
_____
_____

PRAYER: ·····································
_____
_____
_____
_____
_____
_____
_____
_____

WRITE IT DOWN!

JOURNAL IT!

VERSE:

PRAYER:

WRITE IT DOWN!

JOURNAL IT!

VERSE:

_____

_____

_____

_____

_____

_____

_____

_____

_____

_____

_____

_____

_____

_____

_____

PRAYER:

_____

_____

_____

_____

_____

_____

_____

WRITE IT DOWN!

JOURNAL IT!

VERSE:

_____

_____

_____

_____

_____

_____

_____

_____

_____

_____

_____

_____

_____

_____

_____

PRAYER:

_____

_____

_____

_____

_____

_____

_____

WRITE IT DOWN!

JOURNAL IT!

VERSE:

_____

_____

_____

_____

_____

_____

_____

_____

_____

_____

_____

_____

_____

PRAYER: ·······························

_____

_____

_____

_____

_____

_____

_____

WRITE IT DOWN!

JOURNAL IT!

VERSE:

_____

_____

_____

_____

_____

_____

_____

_____

_____

_____

_____

_____

_____

_____

_____

PRAYER:

_____

_____

_____

_____

_____

_____

WRITE IT DOWN!

JOURNAL IT!

VERSE:

_____

_____

_____

_____

_____

_____

_____

_____

_____

_____

_____

_____

_____

_____

_____

PRAYER:

_____

_____

_____

_____

_____

_____

_____

WRITE IT DOWN!　　JOURNAL IT!

VERSE:

PRAYER: ·····················

WRITE IT DOWN!

JOURNAL IT!

VERSE:

_____

_____

_____

_____

_____

_____

_____

_____

_____

_____

_____

_____

_____

PRAYER:

_____

_____

_____

_____

_____

_____

WRITE IT DOWN!

JOURNAL IT!

VERSE:

_____

_____

_____

_____

_____

_____

_____

_____

_____

_____

_____

_____

_____

_____

PRAYER:

_____

_____

_____

_____

_____

_____

WRITE IT DOWN!

JOURNAL IT!

VERSE:

_____

_____

_____

_____

_____

_____

_____

_____

_____

_____

_____

_____

_____

_____

_____

PRAYER:

_____

_____

_____

_____

_____

_____

_____

WRITE IT DOWN!

JOURNAL IT!

VERSE:

_____

_____

_____

_____

_____

_____

_____

_____

_____

_____

_____

_____

_____

_____

_____

PRAYER: ·····································

_____

_____

_____

_____

_____

_____

_____

WRITE IT DOWN!

JOURNAL IT!

VERSE:

_____

_____

_____

_____

_____

_____

_____

_____

_____

_____

_____

_____

_____

_____

PRAYER: ....

_____

_____

_____

_____

_____

_____

_____

WRITE IT DOWN!

JOURNAL IT!

VERSE:

_____

_____

_____

_____

_____

_____

_____

_____

_____

_____

_____

_____

_____

_____

_____

PRAYER:

_____

_____

_____

_____

_____

_____

_____

WRITE IT DOWN!

JOURNAL IT!

VERSE:

_____

_____

_____

_____

_____

_____

_____

_____

_____

_____

_____

_____

_____

_____

_____

PRAYER:

_____

_____

_____

_____

_____

_____

WRITE IT DOWN!

JOURNAL IT!

VERSE:

_____
_____
_____
_____
_____
_____
_____
_____
_____
_____
_____
_____
_____
_____
_____

PRAYER:

_____
_____
_____
_____
_____
_____
_____
_____

WRITE IT DOWN!

JOURNAL IT!

VERSE:

_____

_____

_____

_____

_____

_____

_____

_____

_____

_____

_____

_____

_____

_____

_____

_____

PRAYER:

_____

_____

_____

_____

_____

_____

WRITE IT DOWN!

JOURNAL IT!

VERSE:

_____

_____

_____

_____

_____

_____

_____

_____

_____

_____

_____

_____

_____

_____

_____

PRAYER:

_____

_____

_____

_____

_____

_____

_____

WRITE IT DOWN!

JOURNAL IT!

VERSE:

_____

_____

_____

_____

_____

_____

_____

_____

_____

_____

_____

_____

_____

PRAYER:

_____

_____

_____

_____

_____

_____

WRITE IT DOWN!

JOURNAL IT!

VERSE:

_____

_____

_____

_____

_____

_____

_____

_____

_____

_____

_____

_____

_____

_____

PRAYER: ·····································

_____

_____

_____

_____

_____

_____

_____

WRITE IT DOWN!

JOURNAL IT!

VERSE:

_____

_____

_____

_____

_____

_____

_____

_____

_____

_____

_____

_____

_____

_____

_____

_____

PRAYER:

_____

_____

_____

_____

_____

_____

_____

WRITE IT DOWN!

JOURNAL IT!

VERSE:

_____

_____

_____

_____

_____

_____

_____

_____

_____

_____

_____

_____

_____

PRAYER:

_____

_____

_____

_____

_____

_____

_____

WRITE IT DOWN!

JOURNAL IT!

VERSE:

_____

_____

_____

_____

_____

_____

_____

_____

_____

_____

_____

_____

_____

PRAYER:

_____

_____

_____

_____

_____

_____

_____

WRITE IT DOWN!

JOURNAL IT!

VERSE:

PRAYER:

Made in the USA
Middletown, DE
26 October 2018